THE MINNIE

meadowside 🌿
CHILDREN'S BOOKS

Accept disgrace willingly.

Lao Tsu's Tao Te Ching

It's better to suffer in the beginning
for the pleasure that will come later.

Malay Proverb

He who does not trust enough,
will not be trusted.

Lao Tsu's Tao Te Ching

The worth of a thing is best known
by the want of it.

Thai Proverb

Everyone sees his or her child
as the most beautiful.

Uighur Proverb

You can't lock in wind or woman.

Japanese Proverb

Different flowers look good
to different people.

Chinese Proverb

A child's words have no guile.

Chinese Proverb

One cannot quarrel without an opponent.

Japanese Proverb

When nothing is done,
nothing is left undone.

Lao Tsu's Tao Te Ching

Serve your parents during their lifetime.

Confucius

Too much success is not an advantage.

Lao Tsu's Tao Te Ching

The crow thinks her chick is white,
the hedgehog that her baby is soft.

Uighur Proverb

High winds do not last all morning.
Heavy rain does not last all day.

Lao Tsu's Tao Te Ching

Words have the power to both destroy
and heal. When words are both true
and kind, they can change our world.

Buddha

Even if you hide yourself from the world,
don't lose sight of your true nature.

Okinawan Proverb

BZZZZZZzz!

Keep your mouth shut, guard your senses
and life is ever full.
Open your mouth, always be busy, and life
is beyond hope.

Lao Tsu's Tao Te Ching

Rotten wood cannot be carved.

Chinese Proverb

.

Wisdom comes from brains,
not age.

Uighur Proverb

What is firmly established
cannot be uprooted.
What is firmly grasped
cannot slip away.

Lao Tsu's Tao Te Ching

Forgiving the unrepentant
is like drawing on water.

Japanese Proverb

Learn as if behind, and still be afraid
of losing what has been learned.

Confucius

Cultivate virtue
and virtue will be real.

Lao Tsu's Tao Te Ching

Small things are the most lovable.

Okinawan Proverb

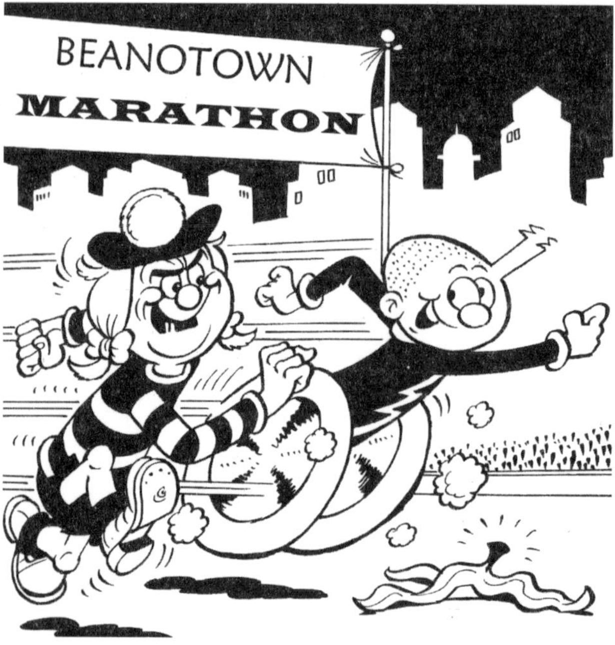
BEANOTOWN
MARATHON

If you are in a hurry,
you will never get there.

Chinese Proverb

The female overcomes the male
with stillness, lying low in stillness.

Lao Tsu's Tao Te Ching

A relative is a relative as long
as relations are maintained.

Uighur Proverb

Open Day:
LADY GERTRUDE'S
ACADEMY FOR
POLITE GIRLS

The reputation of a thousand years
may be determined by
the conduct of one hour.

Japanese Proverb

If you have a clear conscience you won't worry about a knock on the door at night.

Chinese Proverb

When you are ready to learn,
a teacher will appear.

Zen Saying

CRUNCH!

Use attack as the tactic
of defence.

Chinese Proverb

Love the world as your own self,
then you can truly care
for all things.

Lao Tsu's Tao Te Ching

PLOP!

The tongue is more to be feared
than the sword.

Japanese Proverb

The flower that you spent time
to care for does not grow,
while the willow that you accidentally
planted flourishes and gives shade.

Chinese Proverb

Don't do any good to the bad.
Don't expect good from the bad.

Uighur Proverb

Give up learning and put an end
to your troubles.

Lao Tsu's Tao Te Ching

Do good things quickly.

Okinawan Proverb

It's easy to socialise,
much harder to live together.

Chinese Proverb

Courage arises from compassion.

Lao Tsu's Tao Te Ching

Don't turn over the rubbish
to get to a centipede.

Thai Proverb

He who envies others
does not obtain peace of mind.

Buddha

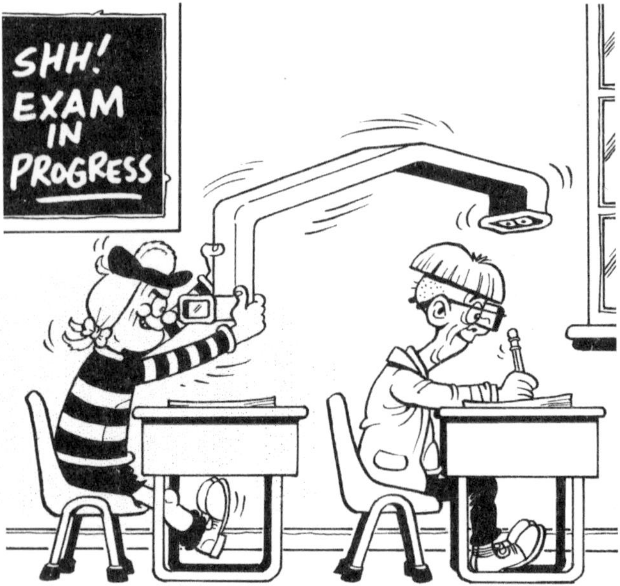
SHH!
EXAM
IN
PROGRESS

It is better to see once
than to hear one hundred times.

Uighur Proverb

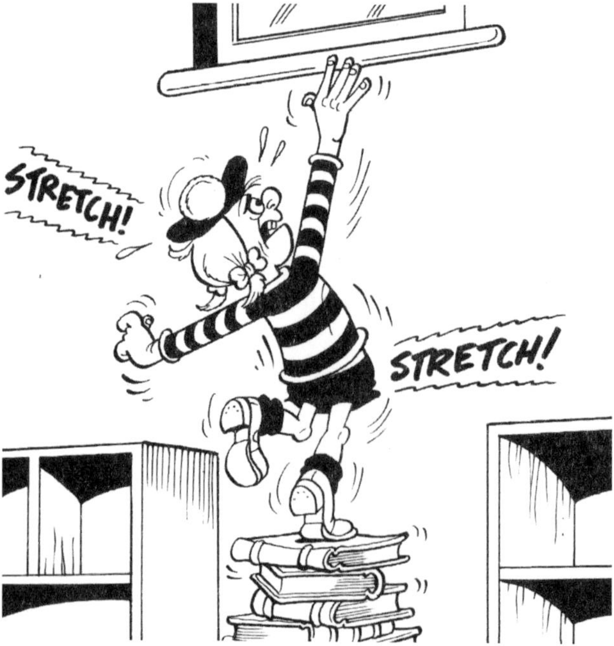
STRETCH!
STRETCH!

Books –
when you need them
you will find you have
too little of them.

Chinese Proverb

Know the strength of men,
but keep a woman's care.

Lao Tsu's Tao Te Ching

One step in the wrong direction
will cause a thousand years of regret.

Chinese Proverb

Pick the flower
when it is ready to be picked.

Chinese Proverb

Sweet words can buy honour.
Good deeds can gain respect.

Lao Tsu's Tao Te Ching

JOIN THE BEANO CLUB. THE MEMBERSHIP IS FOR ONE YEAR AND THE BRONZE MEMBERSHIP PACK INCLUDES...

● A specially designed T-shirt, not available to buy anywhere. Gnasher clockwork chattering teeth.
● A handy tote bag— ideal for sports gear or a packed lunch.
● A frisbee with a difference. Write a message on a magic pad on the **MESSAGE FRISBEE**, and send it by 'airmail' to a friend and wait for their reply.
● Giant size Beano Club poster for your wall.
● A novelty practical joke.
● A Bronze membership card and a wallet to keep it safe.●A pocket - size Beano Club special with two long stories.

DURING THE YEAR YOU'LL ALSO RECEIVE...

● A special Beano Club birthday card from The Beano characters and The Beano Editor.
● Other mail sent from your pals at The Beano.
● Newsletters with competitions, news about other Beano Club members, exclusive offers for members only and inside info about what's going on with the Club or The Beano comic.
● Information about how to become a Silver Member.

PLEASE NOTE:
The contents of the Bronze pack may change from time to time. Allow up to 28 days for delivery. Membership is for one year. To join The Beano Club as a Bronze member, simply log onto

www.beanotown.com

Steve
Anders

Candidate number
P2R/100371

Office of Government Commerce   London:TSO

Applications to reuse, reproduce or republish material in this publication should be sent to HMSO, Licensing Division, St Clement's House, 2-16 Colegate, Norwich, NR3 1BQ

Tel No (01603) 621000   Fax No (01603) 723000

Email: hmsolicensing@cabinet-office.x.gsi.gov.uk, or complete the application form on the HMSO website www.hmso.gov.uk/forms/cform2.htm

HMSO, in consultation with Office of Government Commerce (OGC) will prepare a licence based on standard terms tailored to your particular requirements including payment terms.

PRINCE is a registered trademark of OGC

First edition Crown copyright 1997
Second edition 2002
Second Impression 2002

ISBN 0 11 330916 3 (Single copy ISBN)
ISBN 0 11 330900 7 (Sold in a pack of 10 copies)

For further information regarding this and other OGC products please contact:

OGC Service Desk
Rosebery Court
St Andrews Business Park
Norwich
NR7 0HS
Telephone: +44 (0) 845 000 4999

e-mail: ServiceDesk@ogc.gsi.gov.uk

Website: www.ogc.gov.uk

Printed in the United Kingdom by The Stationery Office
Id 117196 c103 10/02 782445 19585

CONTENTS

INTRODUCTION

Most organisations are experiencing unprecedented levels of change. Change has become a way of life for organisations that need to remain effective and competitive in order to thrive. It is essential to manage the inherent risk associated with change and innovation.

Projects bring together resources, skills, technology and ideas to deliver business benefits or to achieve business objectives. Good project management helps to ensure that these benefits or objectives are achieved within budget, within time and to the required quality.

PRINCE2 is a project management method designed to provide a framework covering the wide variety of disciplines and activities required within a project. The focus throughout PRINCE2 is on the Business Case, which describes the rationale and business justification for the project. The Business Case drives all the project management processes, from initial project set-up through to the finish of the project.

The complete description of PRINCE2 can be found in *Managing Successful Projects with PRINCE2*, published by The Stationery Office. This Pocketbook is produced as an aide-memoire and handy reference for project personnel who are familiar with the method and its terminology.

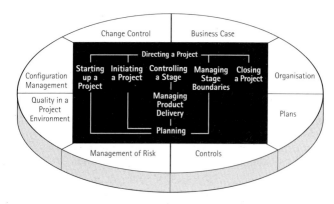

PRINCE2 is a project management method for all types of project. PRINCE2 focuses on the management aspects such as the Business Case, project organisation, plans, controls, quality and risk, and separates these from the specialist task of delivering the outputs of the project (which may include procured products).

PRINCE2 is 'process-based' such that all the project management activities may be easily scaled up or down to suit the requirements of the project.

Throughout the project, PRINCE2 encourages the Project Manager and Project Board to focus on the business justification of the project. At the end of each stage, the Business Case is reviewed to ensure continued viability of the project.

PRINCE2 encourages and supports involvement of the user(s) and all the other stakeholders who have an interest in the project's outcome or who are affected by it in any way.

A PRINCE2 project is sub-divided into stages to provide assessment points for senior management to monitor progress and control the project. The end of a stage represents a key decision and commitment point. The number of stages is totally flexible, based on such considerations as project size, complexity, risk, significance, and criticality.

If the project is part of a programme, PRINCE2 provides the necessary interfaces with programme management.

PRINCE2 is designed to meet requirements of recognised quality management standards.

Customer/Supplier relationship

PRINCE2 assumes that within any project there are various groups of people with specific interests in the project and its outcome, including:

- Customers who have commissioned the work and will be benefiting from the end results
- Users who will use or operate the final product(s). The customer and user may be the same group of people in some situations
- Suppliers who are providing specialist resources and/or skills to the project, or are providing goods and services.

PRINCE2 recognises that the customer and supplier may come from separately managed areas and typically from commercially separate organisations.

Tailoring

PRINCE2's concepts and processes represent good management practices in project management. Each concept and process needs to be applied to suit the specific needs of the project. Tailoring the method involves consideration of such issues as project size, risk, cost, duration, quality, importance, location. Tailoring to suit the circumstances is critical to the successful application of PRINCE2. The philosophy behind each concept and process in PRINCE2 can be applied to the smallest and largest projects.

PROJECT MANAGEMENT PROCESSES

PRINCE2 has eight management processes, each providing a particular emphasis throughout the project lifecycle. Any project run under PRINCE2 will address each of these processes in some form. The processes are not sequential, step-by step, through the project, some can be done in parallel with others. The key to successful use of PRINCE2 is to ask 'How extensively should this process be applied on this project?' for each of the eight processes.

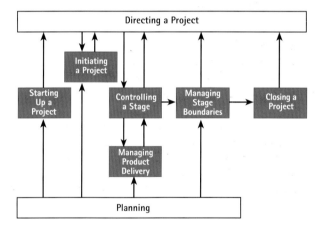

Directing a Project (DP)

This process runs from start-up through to closure of the project and is aimed at the management level above the Project Manager, namely the Project Board. This process defines the Project Board's responsibilities for:

- Approving the Project Brief and authorising initiation
- Authorising the Project Initiation Document, including the Business Case, and taking 'ownership' of the project
- Checking project status at the end of each stage before authorising continuation to the next stage
- Providing management direction and guidance to the Project Manager, and reacting to exception situations
- Liaison with corporate or programme management
- Confirming project closure.

Starting Up a Project (SU)

This is a pre-project process, designed to answer the basic question: 'Do we have a viable and worthwhile project?'. This process will:

- Ensure the necessary authority exists for undertaking the project
- Ensure that sufficient information is available about the project's objectives, scope and constraints
- Design and appoint an appropriate project management team
- Decide on the approach to be used to deliver the required outputs from the project
- Create the initiation Stage Plan.

Initiating a Project (IP)

This is the first real project process and ensures the project can be successfully scoped and managed to its completion by laying down a firm foundation.

This process will:

- Ensure that everyone involved understands the scope and objectives of the project
- Ensure that a suitable Business Case exists for the project
- Ensure that the project has been adequately planned and costed
- Assess the risks identified
- Obtain the commitment from the Project Board to proceed to the next stage.

Controlling a Stage (CS)

This process covers the day-to-day management activities on the project which will be re-iterated throughout the project:

- Authorising work to be done by the project team
- Taking delivery of completed products from the project team
- Monitoring and reporting progress
- Capturing Project Issues
- Assessing required changes
- Taking necessary corrective action.

Managing Product Delivery (MP)

This process breaks the management of the project from the creation or provision of products by the project team:

- Negotiating and accepting Work Packages from the Project Manager
- Ensuring the required work is done

- Reporting on progress
- Ensuring completed products meet required quality criteria
- Obtaining approval for completed products.

Managing Stage Boundaries (SB)

This process covers the Project Manager's responsibilities at the end of each stage, or, if the project is in exception, to enable the Project Board to assess the continued viability of the project:

- Reporting on delivery of products
- Re-assessing the risk situation
- Updating project management documentation
- Planning the next stage, or producing an Exception Plan.

Closing a Project (CP)

This process ensures a clear end to the project whether it is successful completion or early termination:

- Reporting on fulfilment of project objectives defined in the Project Initiation Document
- Recommending required follow-on actions
- Planning post-project review(s)
- Assessing the way the project was managed and reporting lessons learned
- Decommissioning the project.

Planning (PL)

This process describes the iterative steps involved in planning and re-planning the project. It is used during the activities of the other PRINCE2 processes. Planning in PRINCE2 uses the product-based planning technique to ensure plans are based on required outputs (rather than inputs):

- Create a Product Breakdown Structure which identifies the products required
- Write Product Descriptions which include defining the quality requirements for each product
- Draw a Product Flow Diagram which shows the logical order of creation of the products and their interdependencies
- Identify activities required to create the products
- Estimate duration and effort for each activity
- Assess the risks
- Calculate the costs
- Identify management control points needed
- Document the plan, its assumptions and supporting text.

COMPONENTS

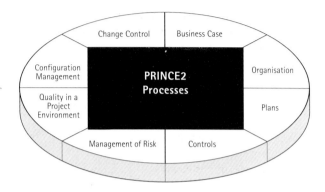

There are a number of key aspects of project management that are used throughout the PRINCE2 processes.

Business Case
A PRINCE2 project is 'driven' by its Business Case which defines the justification and rationale for the project, including the benefits expected and an assessment of costs against these benefits.

The Business Case must embrace all the elements that are affected by the project, not just the most significant element. For example, avoid focussing the Business Case (and hence the project) on the benefits of new equipment whilst ignoring the impact on personnel, accommodation, and changed working practices.

The Business Case is 'owned' by the Executive who is ultimately responsible for the delivery of benefits from the outcome of the project.

Organisation
However small or large the project, there must be agreement on:
- Who says what is needed
- Who provides the budget
- Who provides the resources
- Who authorises changes
- Who manages day-to-day work
- Who defines standards to be met.

On a small project, many of the above will be the responsibility of the same person. On a large project, a number of people may be involved in each of the above. PRINCE2 provides a flexible project management structure consisting of specific roles. Most of these roles may be allocated to one person or shared between a number of people, or combined together.

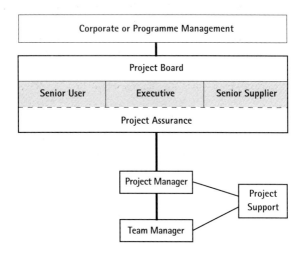

Project Board

The Project Board represents the interests of the business (customer side), user, and supplier, and provides overall direction and management of the project. The Project Board has responsibility and authority for the project within its remit (the Project Mandate) set by corporate or programme management. The Project Board is also responsible for assurance that the project remains on course to deliver the desired outcome as defined in the Business Case.

At the start of a project, the Project Board:
• Approves the Project Brief to commence start-up

- Agrees the Project Manager's responsibilities and objectives
- Decides how Project Assurance is to be carried out
- Commits to resources required for initiation stage
- Confirms project tolerances
- Approves the Project Initiation Document.

As the project progresses, the Project Board:
- Gives direction and guidance to the Project Manager
- Reviews the project status at the end of each stage and approves progress to the next stage
- Checks the project is still on track to achieve the Business Case
- Reviews and approves any exception plans
- Approves changes
- Reports to programme or corporate management
- May recommend project termination.

At the end of the project, the Project Board:
- Checks that all products have been delivered satisfactorily
- Confirms that operational and support groups are prepared to take responsibility for the project's outcome
- Approves the End Project Report, the Lessons Learned Report and the Post Project Review Plan
- Authorises project closure.

The Project Board consists of three roles; Executive, Senior User and Senior Supplier.

Executive

The Executive is the individual with ultimate accountability for the success of the project. The Executive has to ensure that the project represents value for money and follows a cost-conscious approach whilst balancing the needs of the business, the users and the suppliers. The Executive 'owns' the project's Business Case.

Senior User

The Senior User is accountable for ensuring that requirements are fully and accurately specified, making sure that what is delivered is fit for purpose and that the solution meets users' needs within the constraints of the Business Case.

Senior Supplier

This role represents the resources providing design, development, facilitation, procurement, and implementation of the project's products. The Senior Supplier must have the authority to commit or acquire the necessary resources.

Project Manager

The Project Manager has the authority to run the project on a day-to-day basis on behalf of the Project Board. The prime responsibility is to ensure the project delivers the required products to the required standard of quality and within the specified constraints of time and cost.

During the project, the Project Manager will:

- Prepare project documentation including PID, Project and Stage Plans
- Obtain Project Board approval of all plans
- Define responsibilities and allocate work within the project
- Monitor and control progress within tolerance levels agreed with the Project Board
- Manage the risks including development of any required contingency plans
- Negotiate the performance and delivery of Work Packages with the Team Manager(s)
- Schedule stage control points
- Liaise with Project Assurance
- Prepare and present reports for the Project Board, for example at the end of each stage
- Enforce quality and change control procedures
- Ensure Risk, Quality and Issue logs are maintained and used effectively
- Prepare any Exception Plans should tolerance levels be threatened.

Team Manager

This is an optional role, likely to be required on larger projects where teams of different skills are needed. The role may also be relevant where the work of the project is being done by a third party reporting to the customer's Project Manager.

The Team Manager will:
- Negotiate Work Packages with the Project Manager
- Plan and allocate work within the team
- Monitor team progress and initiate any required corrective action
- Report progress and issues to the Project Manager
- Maintain details of quality checks carried out
- Liaise with Project Assurance.

Project Assurance

Project Assurance provides the check that the project continues to meet its specification, the required standards and the Business Case. Project Assurance is the responsibility of each Project Board member, however the role can be delegated, but it must be independent of the Project Manager. Each of the following aspects of Project Assurance should be covered.

Business:
- Focus on the Business Case is maintained
- Risks are being controlled
- Maintenance of liaison between customer and supplier
- Monitoring expenditure and schedule
- Ensuring the project remains viable
- Ensuring the project gives value for money
- Ensuring the project fits with strategy or programme.

User:
- User needs and expectations are being met or managed effectively
- An acceptable solution is being developed.

Specialist:
- Liaison is maintained between customer and supplier
- The needs of the specialist work of the project are recognised
- The scope of the project is not increasing unnoticed
- The required standards are being used correctly and are working.

Project Support

This role may be provided by a dedicated team to the project, or may be provided centrally supporting a number of projects, or may be provided by the Project Manager depending on the size and nature of the project and the capabilities of the organisation.

Project Support covers:
- Configuration management
- Administration of project documentation and control, reviews, meetings and communications
- Providing expertise on support tools, estimating, planning, standards to the Project Manager.

Plans

In PRINCE2 the Project Plan is the only mandatory plan. Most projects will also need Stage Plans and if the project uses a number of teams, there may need to be Team Plans.

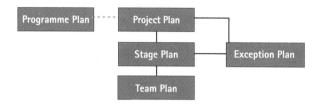

The Project Plan is a high-level document showing the key deliverables and major control points of the project. It summarises the resource requirements and costs and is used by the Project Board as a baseline against which to monitor actual costs and progress through the project.

A Stage Plan contains the level of detail needed for day-to-day control by the Project Manager. Each stage will have a Stage Plan which is produced as the current stage approaches completion.

Team Plans contain the more detailed activities of each Stage Plan and are usually prepared in parallel with the Stage Plan.

An Exception Plan may be produced at any point during a project. If the Project Manager forecasts in an Exception Report that the project may deviate beyond tolerance levels set by the Project Board the board may respond by requesting an Exception Plan. The same thing may happen if it is the Project Plan or a Team Plan that is forecast to exceed its agreed tolerances. The Exception Plan will replace the existing plan showing the work and resources necessary to react to the deviation.

All PRINCE2 plans contain the same information albeit at different levels of detail:
- Graphical summary (such as a Gantt chart)
- Description of the plan
- Prerequisites and assumptions
- External dependencies
- Risks
- Tolerances.

Controls
PRINCE2 controls help to ensure the project is producing the right products and to the right quality, is being carried out according to schedule, and continues to remain viable against its Business Case. The main controls are the following:

Project initiation
Should the project be undertaken?

End stage assessment
Is the project still on course? Are risks under control?

Is the Business Case still viable? Should the next stage be undertaken?

Highlight Reports
Regular reports from the Project Manager for the Project Board.

Exception Reports
Early warning of any forecast deviation beyond tolerance levels.

Project closure
Has the project delivered everything expected? What lessons have been learned?

Stages
The division of the project into stages enables the Project Board to control progress of the project. The Project Board only commits to one stage at a time.

Tolerance
Tolerance is the allowable deviation from a plan without needing to involve higher level management. Tolerance may be set against timescales, costs, scope, quality, risk and benefits. If any plan is forecast to exceed the agreed tolerance levels, the plan is in 'exception'.

Product Descriptions

Product Descriptions define the product to be delivered, the standards to be used or followed, the quality criteria to be applied to ensure the product is fit for purpose and the method to be used to check the product's quality.

Work Package

Work to be done by a project team is specified in a Work Package which requires authorisation from the Project Manager before work can begin.

Project Issues

Project Issues may arise from any situation or source, including:
- User requirements change
- Legislation changes
- Organisation or business changes
- Suppliers being unable to deliver
- Resource availability changes
- Questions or concerns relating to the project.

In PRINCE2, all Project Issues are assessed to determine their impact on the project. All Project Issues raised are logged and any activities required to accommodate or resolve them are managed and documented.

Risk Log

All identified risks are logged and their analysis, countermeasures and status are regularly reviewed by the Project Manager and Project Board.

MANAGEMENT OF RISK

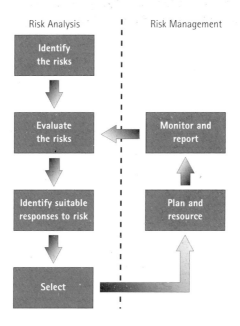

Risk Analysis | Risk Management

- Identify the risks
- Evaluate the risks
- Identify suitable responses to risk
- Select
- Monitor and report
- Plan and resource

The task of risk management is to manage the project's exposure to risk by taking action to keep that exposure to an acceptable level in a cost-effective way.

Risk analysis involves the identification and evaluation of potential risks to any aspect of the project. Having identified the risks, possible actions to deal with the risks need to be considered and appropriate actions selected.

Risk evaluation assesses the probability of the risk occurring and the impact on the project should the risk occur.

Actions to deal with risk include:

- Prevention – Terminate the risk by doing things differently and thus removing the risk, where it is feasible to do so. Countermeasures are put in place that either stop the threat or problem from occurring, or prevent it having any impact on the project or business.
- Reduction – Treat the risk, take action to control it in some way where the actions either reduce the likelihood of the risk developing or limit the impact on the project to acceptable levels.
- Transference – This is a specialist form of risk reduction where the impact of the risk is passed to a third party via, for instance, an insurance policy or penalty clause.
- Acceptance – Tolerate the risk, perhaps because nothing can be done at a reasonable cost to mitigate it, or the likelihood and impact of the risk occurring are at an acceptable level.
- Contingency – These are actions planned and organised to come into force as and when the risk occurs.

Risk management involves planning and implementing the required resources to carry out the selected actions to deal with the risks. Once in place, the actions will require monitoring and reporting to ensure the risk management activities are having the desired effect.

Risk management will be an ongoing activity throughout the project and will involve all members of the project organisation.

QUALITY IN A PROJECT ENVIRONMENT

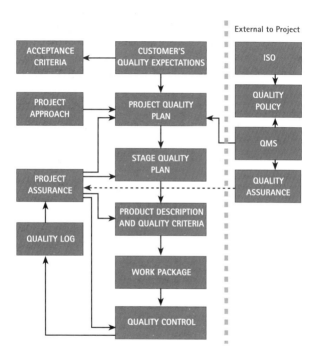

The quality standards and the responsibilities for ensuring quality is built into the project will be derived from a variety of sources including the customer's quality expectations, requirements of ISO standards, and existing quality management systems.

Planning for quality will involve agreement on:

- How each product will be tested against its quality criteria. Defined at the outset of the project.
- When each product will be tested against its quality criteria. Defined in the relevant Stage or Team Plans.
- By whom each product will be tested against its quality criteria. Defined in the relevant Stage or Team Plans.

Quality is achieved by a combination of actions:
- Defining quality criteria for each product in measurable terms
- Developing products according to the defined quality standards
- Checking for quality in all delivered products.

CONFIGURATION MANAGEMENT

Configuration management is a major aspect of achieving quality control on a project. It provides the project with precise control over the project's assets. There are five basic functions within configuration management:

- Planning – deciding the level of detail required
- Identification – specifying all components of the final product
- Control – 'freezing' products and then applying future changes under formal change control
- Status accounting – recording and reporting all current and historical data about each product
- Verification – reviewing and auditing to ensure the actual products match their records.

CHANGE CONTROL

Throughout a project there will be various issues, changes, and queries raised both from within the project and from stakeholders and other external interested parties. Change control provides a formal mechanism for ensuring all Project Issues are logged, considered and appropriate action taken.

Consideration of Project Issues will involve assessing:
- the impact on the project's Business Case and projected benefits
- the impact on identified risks or the creation of new risks
- the impact on cost, time, quality or scope.

Project Issues that identify changes are either Request for Change or Off-Specifications. Requests for Change identify a required change to a product, Off-Specifications identify that a product is likely to fail (or has failed) to achieve its requirements.

GLOSSARY OF PRINCE2 TERMS

Acceptance Criteria
A prioritised list of criteria that the final product(s) must meet before the customer will accept them; a measurable definition of what must be done for the final product to be acceptable to the customer. They should be defined as part of the Project Brief and agreed between customer and supplier no later than the project initiation stage. They should be documented in the Project Initiation Document.

Activity network
A flow diagram showing the activities of a plan and their interdependencies. The network shows each activity's duration, earliest start and finish times, latest start and finish times and float. See also critical path.

Baseline
A snapshot; a position or situation that is recorded. Although the position may be updated later, the baseline remains unchanged and available as a reminder of the original state and as a comparison against the current position. Products that have passed their quality checks and are approved are baselined products. Anything 'baselined' should be under version control in configuration management and 'frozen', i.e. no changes to that version are allowed.

Benefits

The positive outcomes, quantified or unquantified, that a project is being undertaken to deliver, and that justify the investment.

Benefits realisation

The practice of ensuring that the outcome of a project produces the projected benefits claimed in the Business Case.

Business Case

Information that describes the justification for setting up and continuing a PRINCE2 project. It provides the reasons (and answers the question 'Why?') for the project. It is updated at key points throughout the project.

Change authority

A group to which the Project Board may delegate responsibility for the consideration of requests for change. The change authority is given a budget and can approve changes within that budget.

Change budget

The money allocated to the change authority to be spent on authorised requests for change.

Change control

The procedure to ensure that the processing of all Project Issues is controlled, including the submission, analysis and decision making.

Checkpoint
A team-level, time-driven review of progress, usually involving a meeting.

Checkpoint Report
A progress report of the information gathered at a checkpoint meeting, which is given by a team to the Project Manager and provides reporting data as defined in the Work Package.

Communication Plan
Part of the Project Initiation Document describing how the project's stakeholders and interested parties will be kept informed during the project.

Concession
An Off-Specification that is accepted by the Project Board without corrective action.

Configuration audit
A comparison of the latest version number and status of all products shown in the configuration library records against the information held by the product authors.

Configuration management
A discipline, normally supported by software tools, that gives management precise control over its assets (for example, the products of a project), covering planning, identification, control, status accounting and verification of the products.

Configuration status account
A report on the status of products. The required products can be specified by identifier or the part of the project in which they were developed.

Contingency budget
The amount of money required to implement a contingency plan. If the Project Board approves a contingency plan, it would normally set aside a contingency budget, which would only be called upon if the contingency plan had to be implemented.

Contingency plan
A plan that provides an outline of decisions and measures to be taken if defined circumstances, outside the control of a PRINCE2 project, should occur.

Critical path
This is the line connecting the start of a planning network with the final activity in that network through those activities with the smallest float. Often this is a line through the network connecting those activities with a zero float, i.e. those activities where any delay will delay the time of the entire network.

Customer
The person or group who commissioned the work and will benefit from the end results.

Deliverable

An item that the project has to create as part of the requirements. It may be part of the final outcome or an intermediate element on which one or more subsequent deliverables are dependent. According to the type of project, another name for a deliverable is 'product'.

End Project Report

A report given by the Project Manager to the Project Board, that confirms the hand-over of all products and provides an updated Business Case and an assessment of how well the project has done against its Project Initiation Document.

End stage assessment

The review by the Project Board and Project Manager of the End Stage Report to decide whether to approve the next Stage Plan (unless the last stage has now been completed). According to the size and criticality of the project, the review may be formal or informal. The approval to proceed should be documented as an important management product.

End Stage Report

A report given by the Project Manager to the Project Board at the end of each management stage of the project. This provides information about the project performance during the stage and the project status at stage end.

Exception

A situation where it can be forecast that there will be a deviation beyond the tolerance levels agreed between Project Manager and Project Board (or between Project Board and corporate or programme management, or between a Team Manager and the Project Manager).

Exception assessment

This is a meeting of the Project Board to approve (or reject) an Exception Plan.

Exception Plan

This is a plan that often follows an Exception Report. For a Stage Plan exception, it covers the period from the present to the end of the current stage. If the exception were at a project level, the Project Plan would be replaced.

Exception Report

A report that describes an exception, provides an analysis and options for the way forward and identifies a recommended option. The Project Manager presents it to the Project Board.

Executive

The single individual with overall responsibility for ensuring that a project or programme meets its objectives and delivers the projected benefits. This individual should ensure that the project or programme maintains its business focus, that it has clear authority and that the work, including risks, is actively managed. The chairperson of the Project Board, representing the customer and owner of the Business Case.

Feasibility study
A feasibility study is an early study of a problem to assess if a solution is feasible. The study will normally scope the problem, identify and explore a number of solutions and make a recommendation on what action to take. Part of the work in developing options is to calculate an outline Business Case for each as one aspect of comparison.

Follow-on Action Recommendations
A report that can be used as input to the process of creating a Business Case/Project Mandate for any follow-on PRINCE2 project and for recording any follow-on instructions covering incomplete products or outstanding issues. It also sets out proposals for post-project review of the project's products.

Gantt chart
This is a diagram of a plan's activities against a time background, showing start and end times and resources required.

Gate review
A generic term, rather than a PRINCE2 term, meaning a point at the end of a stage or phase where a decision is made whether to continue with the project. In PRINCE2 this would equate to an end stage assessment.

Highlight Report
Report from the Project Manager to the Project Board on a time-driven frequency on stage progress.

Issue Log
A log of all Project Issues including requests for change raised during the project, showing details of each issue, its evaluation, what decisions about it have been made and its current status.

Lessons Learned Report
A report that describes the lessons learned in undertaking the project and that includes statistics from the quality control of the project's management products. It is approved by the Project Board and then held centrally for the benefit of future projects.

Off-Specification
Something that should be provided by the project, but currently is not (or is forecast not to be) provided. This might be a missing product or a product not meeting its specification.

Outcome
The term used to describe the totality of what the project is set up to deliver, consisting of all the specialist products. For example, this could be an installed computer system with trained staff to use it, backed up by new working practices and documentation, a refurbished and equipped building with all the staff moved in and working, or it

could be a new product launched with a recruited and trained sales and support team in place.

Peer review
Peer reviews are specific reviews of a project or any of its products where personnel from within the organisation and/or from other organisations carry out an independent assessment of the project. Peer reviews can be done at any point within a project but are often used at stage-end points.

Phase
A part, section or segment of a project, similar in meaning to a PRINCE2 stage. The key meaning of stage in PRINCE2 terms is the use of management stages, i.e. sections of the project to which the Project Board only commits one at a time. A phase might be more connected to a time slice, change of skills required or change of emphasis.

Post-implementation review
See Post-project review.

Post-project review
One or more reviews held after project closure to determine if the expected benefits have been obtained. Also known as post-implementation review.

PRINCE2

A method that supports some selected aspects of project management. The acronym stands for PRojects IN Controlled Environments.

PRINCE2 project

A project whose product(s) can be defined at its start sufficiently precisely so as to be measurable against predefined metrics and that is managed according to the PRINCE2 method.

Process

That which must be done to bring about a particular outcome, in terms of information to be gathered, decisions to be made and results that must be achieved.

Producer

This role represents the creator(s) of a product that is the subject of a quality review. Typically, it will be filled by the person who has produced the product or who has led the team responsible.

Product

Any input to or output from a project. PRINCE2 distinguishes between management products (which are produced as part of the management or quality processes of the project) and specialist products (which are those products that make up the final deliverable). A product may itself be a collection of other products.

Product based planning
A three step diagrammatic technique leading to a comprehensive plan based on creation and delivery of required outputs. The technique considers pre-requisite products, quality requirements and the dependencies between products.

Product Breakdown Structure
A hierarchy of all the products to be produced during a plan.

Product Checklist
A list of the major products of a plan, plus key dates in their delivery.

Product Description
A description of a product's purpose, composition, derivation and quality criteria. It is produced at planning time, as soon as the need for the product is identified.

Product Flow Diagram
A diagram showing the sequence of production and interdependencies of the products listed in a Product Breakdown Structure.

Programme
A portfolio of projects selected, planned and managed in a co-ordinated way.

Project
A temporary organisation that is created for the purpose of delivering one or more business products according to a specified Business Case.

Project Assurance
The Project Board's responsibilities to assure itself that the project is being conducted correctly.

Project Brief
A description of what the project is to do; a refined and extended version of the Project Mandate, which has been agreed by the Project Board and which is input to project initiation.

Project closure notification
Advice from the Project Board to inform the host location that the project resources can be disbanded and support services, such as space, equipment and access, demobilised.

Project closure recommendation
Notification prepared by the Project Manager for the Project Board to send (when the board is satisfied that the project can be closed) to any organisation that has supplied facilities to the project.

Project Initiation Document (PID)
A logical document which brings together the key information needed to start the project on a sound basis

and to convey that information to all concerned with the project.

Project Issue
A term used to cover either a general issue, query, a Request for Change, suggestion or Off-Specification raised during a project. Project Issues can be about anything to do with the project.

Project management
The planning, monitoring and control of all aspects of the project and the motivation of all those involved in it to achieve the project objectives on time and to the specified cost, quality and performance.

Project management team
A term to represent the entire management structure of Project Board, Project Manager, plus any Team Manager, Project Assurance and Project Support roles.

Project Manager
The person given the authority and responsibility to manage the project on a day-to-day basis to deliver the required products within the constraints agreed with the Project Board.

Project Mandate
Information created externally to the project, which forms the terms of reference and is used to start up the PRINCE2 project.

Project Plan

A high-level plan showing the major products of the project, when they will be delivered and at what cost. An initial Project Plan is presented as part of the Project Initiation Document. This is revised as information on actual progress appears. It is a major control document for the Project Board to measure actual progress against expectations.

Project Quality Plan

A plan defining the key quality criteria, quality control and audit processes to be applied to project management and specialist work in the PRINCE2 project. It will be part of the text in the Project Initiation Document.

Project records

A collection of all approved management, specialist and quality products and other material, which is necessary to provide an auditable record of the project.

NB This does not include working files.

Project start-up notification

Advice to the host location that the project is about to start and requesting any required Project Support services.

Project Support Office

A group set up to provide certain administrative services to the Project Manager. Often the group provides its services to many projects in parallel.

Quality

The totality of features and characteristics of a product or service that bear on its ability to satisfy stated and implied needs. Also defined as 'fitness for purpose' or 'conforms to requirements'.

Quality Management System

The complete set of quality standards, procedures and responsibilities for a site or organisation.

Quality review

A quality review is a quality checking technique with a specific structure, defined roles and procedure designed to ensure a product's completeness and adherence to standards. The participants are drawn from those with an interest in the product and those with the necessary skills to review its correctness. An example of the checks made by a quality review is 'Does the document match the quality criteria in the Product Description?'

Quality system

See Quality Management System.

Request for Change

A means of proposing a modification to the current specification of a product. It is one type of Project Issue.

Reviewer

A person asked to review a product that is the subject of a quality review.

Risk Log

A document that provides identification, estimation, impact evaluation and countermeasures for all risks to the project. It should be created during the start-up of the project and developed during the life of the project. Also known as Risk Register.

Risk profile

A graphical representation of information normally found on the Risk Log.

Risk register

See Risk Log.

Senior Responsible Owner

This is not a PRINCE2 term, but is used in many organisations. Its equivalent in PRINCE2 terms would be the 'Executive' role.

Senior Supplier

The Project Board role that provides knowledge and experience of the main discipline(s) involved in the production of the project's deliverable(s). Represents the supplier(s) interests within the project and provides supplier resources.

Senior User

A member of the Project Board, accountable for ensuring that user needs are specified correctly and that the solution meets those needs.

Sponsor

Not a specific PRINCE2 role but often used to mean the major driving force of a project. May be the equivalent of Executive or corporate/programme management.

Stakeholders

Parties with an interest in the execution and outcome of a project. They would include business streams affected by or dependent on the outcome of a project.

Supplier

The group or groups responsible for the supply of the project's specialist products.

Team Manager

A role that may be employed by the Project Manager or a specifically appointed alternative person to manage the work of project team members.

Tolerance

The permissible deviation above and below a plan's estimate of time and cost without escalating the deviation to the next level of management. Separate tolerance figures should be given for time and cost. There may also be tolerance levels for quality, scope, benefit and risk. Tolerance is applied at project, stage and team levels.

User(s)

The person or group who will use the final deliverable(s) of the project.

Work Package

The set of information relevant to the creation of one or more products. It will contain the Product Description(s), details of any constraints on production such as time and cost, interfaces and confirmation of the agreement between the Project Manager and the person or Team Manager who is to implement the Work Package that the work can be done within the constraints.